鄭辛遙幽默畫

ZHENG XINYAO
HUMOUROUS
CARTOONS

智慧快餐

1

上海人民出版社

SHANGHAI PEOPLE'S PUBLISHING HOUSE

Simplicity——the starting point and the terminal point of the art.

Zheng Xinyao, member of the Artist Association of China, member of the Shanghai Cartoon Art Committee, member of the board of editors of *Cartoon World,* art editor of the *Xinmin Evening Newspaper.*
Works won the prize in some international cartoon exhibiting competitions held in Belgium, Italy and Japan. Used to be one of the judges of the Bulgaria No. 9 International Cartoon Competition. In 1991, published *Zheng Xinyao's Humour Cartoon.* In 1992, held personal homour cartoon exhibitions in Belgium, German and other countries. In 1994, the 'Wisdom Snack'Cartoon Set won the prize in the No. 8 National Excellent Art Work Exhibition. In 1995, the 'Wisdom Snack' Cartoon Set won the No. 3 Shanghai Literature Art Prize (Outstanding Achievement prize).

简——是艺术的起点和终点

郑辛遥,中国美术家协会会员,上海漫画艺术委员会委员,
《漫画世界》编委,新民晚报社美术编辑。

作品在比利时、意大利、日本等国际漫画展览比赛中获
奖。曾任保加利亚第九届国际漫画大赛的评委。1991年出版
《郑辛遥幽默画》作品集,1992年赴比利时、德国等国家举办个
人幽默漫画展。1994年《智慧快餐》系列漫画在第八届全国优
秀美术作品展览中获奖。1995年《智慧快餐》系列漫画获第三
届上海文学艺术奖(优秀成果奖)。

AUTHOR'S PREFACE

The maxim is the extract of human beings' thought and language, and is rich in nourishment. In this maxim world which is vast as the open sea, I am a 'panner', also a 'gleener and scrap-collector'. After I arranged all the maxims of the famous, epigrams of the ordinary and folk proverbs I picked, I recreated them, mixed my thoughts and feelings about the life together with the pictures, and tried my best to make the pictures and writting into a kind of embossed humour art.

Nowadays life rhythm is speedy, people are eager to have more wisdom, so as to make their life more happy and relaxed. No matter in the real life or in books, the masses like 'snack' culture, and that is my original intention to create the 'Wisdom Snack'. In the end of 1992, I opened up the special column—— 'Wisdom Snack' in the supplement of the *Xinmin Evening Newspaper.* Due to the great likes of the editors, in addition to the frequent encouragement from my colleagues and readers, the special column has been published once a week since then and has never been suspended. Now thanks to the Shanghai People's Publishing House, the 'Wisdom Snack' is collected in this volume to be tasted. May its popularity be as great as its worth deserves.

Xin Yao.

1995 Autumn

自序

    格言是人类思想和语言的浓缩品，蕴含着丰富的营养。在浩如烟海的格言世界里，我是一个"淘金者"，也是一个"拾荒者"。对采撷来的名人格言、凡人警句和民间谚语，进行思考整理再创作，把自己对生活、对人生的一点感悟融入画面，力求使图画与文字成为凹凸相嵌的幽默艺术。

    当今时代生活节奏加快，人们渴望多一点智慧，令自己生活得轻松愉快。大众无论在生活中还是书本里，都喜欢"快餐"文化，这就是我创作"智慧快餐"的初衷。1992 年 10 月我在《新民晚报》副刊上开辟了"智慧快餐"专栏，由于编辑的厚爱，加之常得到同行和读者的鼓励，每周一幅，连载至今。现蒙上海人民出版社汇编成册，奉大家品赏。

一九九五年秋

智慧——她使您的嘴巴线条朝上。

Wisdom turns the corners of your mouth up.

FOOD FOR THOUGHT

智慧快餐

自由就是这样的东西，你不给予别人，自己也无法
得到。

Freedom is something that you won't get if you don't give.

FOOD FOR THOUGHT
智慧快餐

只知道自己不做坏事,不知道别人会做坏事,这样的人难免要吃大亏。

Such a person will inevitably suffer heavy losses who only knows not to do evil himself, but does not know that others would do evil.

所谓礼貌，就是彼此调节到适当的距离。

The so-called courtesy is to adjust each other to a suitable distance.

请息掉怒气! 愤怒只会把人锁在他自己的房子里。

Calm down! Anger can only lock a man in his own house.

FOOD FOR THOUGHT

智慧快餐

许多人不了解自己，却又想方设法去了解别人。

Many people don't understand themselves, but they try their best to understand others.

FOOD FOR THOUGHT

智慧快餐

一旦撒了一次谎，就需要有很好的记忆，全力把它记住。

Once you tell a lie, you have to have a very good memory, and try your best to memorize your lie.

FOOD FOR THOUGHT

智慧快餐

懂得怎样解决问题的人，工作效率永远赶不上懂得怎样避开问题的人。

Those who know how to solve the problem are always less efficient than those who know how to keep away from the problem.

FOOD FOR THOUGHT
智慧快餐

简单的事情考虑得很复杂，可发现新的领域；复杂的现象看得很简单，可发现新定律。

To consider simple things complicatedly, you may find new fields, to regard complicated phenomenon as something simple, you may discover new laws.

一个人最大的缺点就是一点缺点也没有。

One's biggest shortcoming is that he has no shortcoming at all.

奸商是一种须加倍提防的人，尤其是当你和他们握过手之后，得数一下自己的手指头。

Unscrupulous merchants is a kind of persons you have to beware of doubly, especially after shaking hands with them, you'd better count your fingers.

FOOD FOR THOUGHT
智慧快餐

自以为不会跌下来的人，其实他迟早会跌下来。

One who thinks that he will not fall down will actually fall down sooner or later.

"赚钱游戏"的规则应定在不能让你一下子赢得太多，这样就可避免一下子输得太惨。

The regulation of 'money-making game' should be formulated as follows: you are not permitted to win too much, thus you may avoid to lose too much at a time.

FOOD FOR THOUGHT

智慧快餐

觉悟者告诫我们：无所得，即是得；以是得，无所得。

The awakened admonish us: to get nothing is to get something; to
have got something is to get nothing.

FOOD FOR THOUGHT
智慧快餐

有时放得下比拿得起更需要一种力量。

Sometimes it needs more power to lay down than to take up.

对男人一知半解的女人,最后做了男人的妻子;对男人什么都了解的女人,最后便成了……

Those women who have a smattering knowledge about men be-
come men's wives at last; those who know men thoroughly be-
come... at last.

FOOD FOR THOUGHT

智慧快餐

与其说要改变一种常态，倒不如说由另一种状态
来取代。

It's better to say to replace with another condition than to want
to change a kind of normal behavior.

FOOD FOR THOUGHT
智慧快餐

当你刻意模仿潇洒的时候，正是你离潇洒最远的时候。

When you imitate smartness purposely, it is the time you stay away farthest from the smartness.

拥有好心境的人，才是真正的富有者。

Those who are in a good mood are real men of wealth.

发生争吵和埋怨,是因为平等的人们没有分到平等的东西,或者不平等的人们分到了平等的东西。

When quarrel and complaint happens, either because equal people fail to share the equal thing, or unequal people share the equal thing.

FOOD FOR THOUGHT

智慧快餐

如果明了"祸福无常"这个道理，就不会因一时的
走运而得意忘形。

If one has realized the reason that 'weal and woe is variable', he
will not go wild with glee for the momentary fortune.

FOOD FOR THOUGHT
智慧快餐

在某些女人眼里，成功的男人就是赚的钱比太太
花的要多，失败的男人则相反。

In some women's eyes, a successful man earns more money than
his wife spends, an unsuccessful man does the contrary.

FOOD FOR THOUGHT
智慧快餐

测验一个人的智力是否属上乘，只要看他脑子里
是否同时容纳反向思维。

To know whether someone's IQ is high or not, just watch if he is
able to do reverse thinking.

FOOD FOR THOUGHT

智慧快餐

盲目崇拜别人和随意贬低别人，其实都是缺乏自信的表现。

To worship others blindly and belittle others at will are both factually the display of lack of self-confidence.

会犯错的是人，能原谅人的是神。

It´s men who make mistakes. It´s God who forgives men.

男人的某些"狡猾"，往往是被女人逼出来的。

Men's some 'craftiness' is often squeezed by women.

恋爱其实是一种严重的精神病，只能靠结婚来
治愈。

Love is actually a serious mental disorder. It can only be cured by marriage.

FOOD FOR THOUGHT
智慧快餐

一个愚蠢的人总是能找到一个更愚蠢的人来崇
拜他。

A stupid person can always find a more stupid person to admire
him.

你是否被上司所赏识，只要看在你下面加人，还是在你上面加人。

To see if you are appreciated by your boss, just watch whether he puts people above you or below you.

人们常说时间流逝，其实不对。时间是静止的，流逝的是我们。

It is often said that time elapses. But actually it does not. Time stays put. We elapse.

腾不出时间娱乐的人，迟早会腾出时间来生病。

Those who can't find time to have fun will sooner or later find time to get ill.

我们每个人其实都是无知的，只是无知的方面有别罢了。

In fact, every one of us is ignorant, just the aspect of ignorance is different.

FOOD FOR THOUGHT

智慧快餐

始终要记住：别把你的头抬得比帽子还高。

Always remember, don't hold your head higher than your hat.

FOOD FOR THOUGHT

智慧快餐

规则一：顾客永远是对的。规则二：如果顾客有错，再读规则一。

Rule One: Customer is always right. Rule Two: When customer is not right reread Rule One.

电脑对人来说，它的缺点是没有感情，但优点呢？
还是没有感情。

For human beings, the shortcoming of a computer is no feeling.
What about its advantage? Still no feeling.

要是你们之间无话可说，就分享你们所共有的其他东西吧——沉默。

If you have nothing to say between you two, then share the else you have——silence.

幸福在哪里?幸福就是在太多和太少之间的一站。

Where is happiness? Happiness is the stop between too much and too few.

FOOD FOR THOUGHT

智慧快餐

为了跳到天上去，必须让你的双脚先坚定地踩在大地上。

Before jumping up to the sky, you have to let your feet stand on the ground firmly.

聪明人能认识已经发生的事，而天才能认识将要
发生的事。

Smart people can understand what has already happened. Only
a genius can foresee what will happen.

FOOD FOR THOUGHT

智慧快餐

一个人什么都能逃避，唯独逃避不了他自身。

One can escape anything but himself.

一扇门如果被关上，必定还有另一扇窗会打开。

If a door is closed, there must be a window opened up.

FOOD FOR THOUGHT

智慧快餐

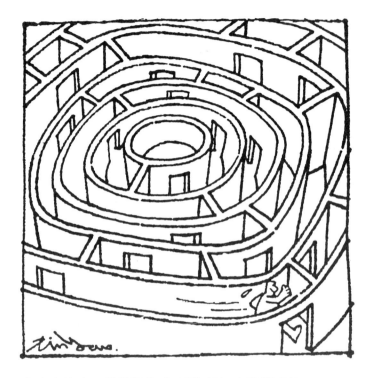

人生之路由无数道门构成, 看你如何走出和进入。

The way of life is made up of countless gates, it depends on how you get out and enter.

FOOD FOR THOUGHT

智慧快餐

该知道的，还是让大家知道为好。

Let people know what they ought to know.

FOOD FOR THOUGHT

智慧快餐

人生犹如时钟一般,他的完美不在于走得快,而在于走得准。

Life is like a clock, its perfection does not depend on its speed, but its accuracy.

FOOD FOR THOUGHT

智慧快餐

有些人一生中所犯的错误都是在本想说"不"的
时候说了"是"。

The mistake some people made during their lifetime is that they
said 'yes' while they actually wanted to say 'no'.

FOOD FOR THOUGHT

智慧快餐

结婚的真正基础是彼此误会。至于离婚,才是双方
经过深入了解之后的结果。

The real reason for getting married is mutual misunderstanding. As
to divorce it is the consequence of real mutual understanding.

FOOD FOR THOUGHT

智慧快餐

爱情之酒，两人喝是甘露；三人喝是酸醋；随便喝要中毒。

The wine of love tastes sweet for two, tastes sour for three, and is poisonous for casual drinkers.

我们常常抗议不公正的批评，却乐意接受不应得的赞誉。

We often protest unfair critics. But we are pleased to accept undeserved praises.

无知是这么一种东西：当你拥有它时，你就会有吓人的胆量。

Ignorance is such a thing: when you possess it, you have terrific guts.

有时，思想也会在未成熟时就从树上掉下来。

Sometimes thoughts will also fall off the tree before they are matured.

在这个世界上成功的最好途径，就是遵照阁下自己劝告别人的话去做。

The best route to success in this world is to follow the advice that you give to others.

好主意的缺点是：它很快就沦为辛苦的工作。

The defect of a good idea is that it will quickly turn into hard work.

FOOD FOR THOUGHT

智慧快餐

我们经常地是由于自身的缺点而不是优点招人喜欢。

We are adored usually because of our weaknesses, instead of merits.

FOOD FOR THOUGHT
智慧快餐

得宠的傻瓜总是"聪明"的。

The idiots who gain favour are always 'smart'.

除非你弯下腰，否则别人是不可能骑上你的背的。

Others can't ride on your back unless you bow.

FOOD FOR THOUGHT

聪明人嘲笑傻瓜，傻瓜也嘲笑聪明人，双方会感到
同等的快乐。

The smart laugh at the stupid. The stupid laugh at the smart. Both
sides feel the same joy.

孤独者有个特点，他不爱别人的同时还不愿接受
别人的爱。

A loner has a character, he does not love others, meanwhile he
is not willing to accept love from others.

FOOD FOR THOUGHT
智慧快餐

听人说话只信一半，是精明；知道哪一半可信，才
是聪明。

It is astute to believe only a half when listening to others, and it is
wise to know which half could be believed.

脑子里装满着自己,这样的人正是那种最空虚的人。

The person whose mind is filled up with himself is in fact empty.

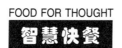

追求别人表面上的赞赏，就是将自己的快乐委诸别人手中。

To seek other's outward praise equals to consign your own happiness to others' hands.

幸福不在我们身外，但是我们常向身外找。幸福原在我们心中，但是我们少往心中寻。

Happiness can't be found outside of us. But we usually look for it from outside. It can be found inside of us. But we seldom look for it from inside.

FOOD FOR THOUGHT
智慧快餐

女人是用耳朵恋爱的，而男人却是用眼睛恋爱的。

Women fall in love by ears and men fall in love by eyes.

FOOD FOR THOUGHT

智慧快餐

一个人为寻求他所需要的东西，走遍了全世界，回到家里找到了。

Man travels all around the world looking for what he wants. He finds them when he is back home.

FOOD FOR THOUGHT
智慧快餐

从崇高到荒唐只有一步，可是从荒唐却没有路能
回到崇高。

With only one step, you can change the sublime to the absurd.
But there is absolutely no way to get back from the absurd to the
sublime.

FOOD FOR THOUGHT

人的一生中可能犯的最大错误，就是经常担心犯错误。

The biggest mistake that a man might make in his life is that he often worrys about making mistakes.

打开幸福之门的唯一钥匙并非是金钱，但如果有
足够的金钱，那便可以定做一把钥匙。

The only key to the door of happiness is not money, but if you
have enough money, then you can order a key.

FOOD FOR THOUGHT

智慧快餐

如果你能花钱解决问题，那你根本就没有问题。

If you can solve problems by spending money, then in effect you
don't have problems.

FOOD FOR THOUGHT
智慧快餐

生气的后果永远比生气的原因严重。如擦伤引起
的争吵几乎总是以刺伤告结束。

The result of getting angry is always more serious than the cause of
getting angry. For example, a quarrel caused by a scrape always
ends up with a stab.

FOOD FOR THOUGHT

智慧快餐

人越是接近真理，越能包容别人。

Closer is a man to the truth, more broad-minded is he to other people.

谁都能够同情朋友的痛苦，但同情朋友的成功，就
要有非常高贵的品格了。

Everybody can sympathize the sufferings of a friend. But it needs
very noble personality to sympathize the successes of a friend.

FOOD FOR THOUGHT
智慧快餐

交朋友的唯一方法是你自己首先要够朋友。

The only way of making friend is that you yourself should deserve
to be called a true friend at first.

当女人的美眸被泪水蒙住时，看不清的是男人。

When the beautiful eyes of women are covered with tears, it's men who can't see.

人世间相距最远的两点，是两颗隔膜的心。

The most remote two points in this world are two estranged hearts.

FOOD FOR THOUGHT
智慧快餐

在前半生里，人们向前看后半生；而在后半生里，
人们向后看前半生。

During the first half of life, people look ahead to the second half.
But during the second half of life, people look back to the first half.

时间在我们背后，时间在我们前面，但它不在我们身旁。

Time may be behind us. Time may be before us. But it is never beside us.

女人常把问题放在心里，男人则把问题放在脑子里。

Women usually put problems in the heart. While men put problems in the brain.

过分地急于还礼,其实是一种忘恩的行为。

Being overly eager to return favor is in fact an act of ungrateful-
ness.

有的人有两个我：一个在黑暗里醒着，一个在光明中睡着。

Some people have two selves. One is awake in the darkness. The other is asleep in the daylight.

FOOD FOR THOUGHT

智慧快餐

如同人无法举起自己的身体，人也无法赞扬自己。

Just as men can't lift up their own bodies, men can't boast about them selves.

FOOD FOR THOUGHT

如果你能找到人人都同意的事情，那毫无疑问这
事情一定是错的。

If you can find something that everybody agrees on, without a
doubt, this must be something incorrect.

FOOD FOR THOUGHT

如果你唯一的工具是把锤子，你往往会把一切问题都看成钉子。

If the only tool you have is a hammer, you will tend to think that all the problems are nails.

FOOD FOR THOUGHT

智慧快餐

如果两个人意见始终一致的话，那么其中的一个
是属于不必存在的人。

If two persons agree on everything, then one of them need not
exist.

当你觉得束手无策时，不妨换一个地方挖个洞，
从一个不同的角度看问题。

When you are at your wit's end, you might as well dig a hole in
another location. To view the problem from a different angle.

FOOD FOR THOUGHT
智慧快餐

不要常把人分成好人和坏人，通常只有讨人喜欢
和不讨人喜欢的人之分。

Don't divide people into good and bad. In fact there are only
people who are likable and those not.

当没有人看到你的时候，你才是真正的你。

When nobody is around, you are your true self.

FOOD FOR THOUGHT

男人想找个十全十美的女人，但问题是女人多半
也想找个十全十美的男人。

Man wants to find a perfect woman. But the problem is that most
of those women want to find a perfect man.

FOOD FOR THOUGHT

智慧快餐

过度的休息和缺少休息同样会使人疲倦不堪。

Both the over-rest and the lack of rest makes one exhausted.

经常原谅别人的人，他的心田一定会保持滋润。

If a man often forgives others, surely his heart will keep moistened.

FOOD FOR THOUGHT

智慧快餐

记住，报复也是受别人控制的一种方式。

Remember, revenge is also a way of being controlled by others.

FOOD FOR THOUGHT
智慧快餐

有时候，我们以为自己厌恶恭维，实际上，我们只是讨厌恭维的方式而已。

Sometimes, we think we dislike flatteries. Actually we just don't like the way that flatteries are presented.

失败的人只有两种：一种是不听任何人的话；另一种是任何人的话都听。

There are two kinds of persons who will fail. One listens to nobody. The other listens to everybody.

雅量是接受不能改变的事实，勇气是改变能改变
的事情，而智慧则是区分这两者的不同。

Generosity is to accept unchangeable facts, courage is to
change changeable matters, wisdom is to distinguish the differ-
ence between the above two.

受了别人的气以后可以有种种反应，最有技巧而
最不费力的是沉默不语。

After being offended by others you can have all kinds of reac-
tions, among them silence is the most skillful and laboursaving.

FOOD FOR THOUGHT

智慧快餐

男人们喜欢追逐像浴缸里的湿肥皂般难以捉摸的女人，即使是讨厌洗澡的男人。

Men love to chase women who are as slippery as wet soap in the tub, even if those who dislike taking a bath.

假如你拥有两支箭的话，往往会因依赖第二支而不在乎第一支。

If you have two arrows, you often do not care the first one because you rely on the second one.

对小事毫无兴趣的人常常会对大事发生错误的
兴趣。

Those who are not interested in trifles often have mistaken interest
to great events.

相信金钱无所不能的人，常常为了钱而无所不为。

Those who believe that money is almighty, often stop at nothing for money.

道德常常能弥补智慧的缺陷，而什么东西可以弥补道德的缺陷呢？

Moral can often make up for the defect of wisdom, but what can make up for the defect of moral?

除了知道把握时机以外，一生中最重要的事就是
要知道应该在什么时候放弃好处。

In addition to knowing how to seize opportunities, the most important thing in life is to know when to give up your interests.

很多显得像朋友的人其实不是朋友，而很多是朋友的并不显得像朋友。

Many who look like friends are actually not friends. Many who don't look like friends are in fact friends.

FOOD FOR THOUGHT

智慧快餐

醉汉莫往下看，否则连路也不会走。

The drunken man can't look down, otherwise he can't even walk.

FOOD FOR THOUGHT
智慧快餐

对某些男人来说，情人就是瓶中的酒，老婆不过是
一个酒瓶而已。

For some men, a lover is the wine in the bottle and the wife is only
the bottle.

FOOD FOR THOUGHT

智慧快餐

生活就是这样充满遗憾，当你擦玻璃时，脏的总是
在另一面。

Life is always full of regrets. When you are cleaning the window,
dirt is always on the other side.

世界上最大的待开发地就在你的帽子下面。

The biggest place in the world that needs to be exploited is under your hat.

FOOD FOR THOUGHT

智慧快餐

每个人都埋怨自己的记忆力，却无人埋怨自己的
判断力。

Everyone complains about his memory. But nobody complains
about his judgment.

FOOD FOR THOUGHT

智慧快餐

越是善良的人，往往越察觉不出别人的居心不良。

The more one is kind, the less he can realize others' evil intentions.

有些人的脑袋,就像他们的帽子一样,很容易被风
吹走。

Some people´s minds, just like their hats, could easily be blown
away by wind.

FOOD FOR THOUGHT

智慧快餐

人们从一条锁链中挣脱出来，只是为了被另一条锁链锁住。

People get rid of one pair of shackles just in order to be tied up by another.

勤奋：比你的上司早半小时上班。聪明：比你的上司先半分钟到达。

Being diligent means coming to work half an hour earlier than boss. Being smart means arriving half a minute earlier than boss.

使你疲倦的不是前面的高山，而是你鞋里的一粒
石子。

What makes you tired is not the high mountain in front of you, but
the stone in your shoe.

FOOD FOR THOUGHT
智慧快餐

许多人在重组自己的偏见时，还以为自己在思考呢。

A lot of people think they are reflecting, but in fact they are re-shaping their prejudice.

FOOD FOR THOUGHT

智慧快餐

何谓爱情?两心一体。何谓友情?两体一心。

Love is one body with two hearts. Friendship is one heart with two bodies.

FOOD FOR THOUGHT

智慧快餐

即使你的朋友像蜂蜜那么甜，你也不能把他完全
舔完。

Even if your Friend is as sweet as honey. You shouldn't lick him off.

闲话是什么?它的公式是——二加二等于五。

What is a gossip? It's formula is——two plus two equals five.

对说谎者的惩罚，并不在于别人不相信他，而是他
不能相信别人。

The punishmen to a liar is not that others do not believe him, but
that he can't believe others.

信仰就是相信眼睛看不见的东西，而信仰的报酬
就是能看得见相信的事。

The belief is to believe what you can't see. The reward of belief is
to see what you believe.

FOOD FOR THOUGHT
智慧快餐

一条鱼的施赠，仅能应付一餐之需；授予捕鱼之术，将使他人终身受益。

The grant of one fish can only meet the need of one meal. But it can be lifelong benefit if you teach others how to catch fishes.

FOOD FOR THOUGHT

智慧快餐

由于机器变得愈来愈像人，人也会变得愈来愈像机器了。

Machines are becoming more and more like human beings, and vice versa.

FOOD FOR THOUGHT

智慧快餐

广告就是卖的艺术，任何人要跨进这个行业就得
要有把自己也卖掉的能力。

Advetising is the art of selling. Anyone who wants to be in this
business should have the ability to sell himself.

在你必须作出选择时并没有这样做，这本身就是
一种选择。

It in itself is a choice that you don't make a choice when you
have to.

FOOD FOR THOUGHT

智慧快餐

怕别人笑自己的人连小丑都不如。

You will be inferior than a clown if you are afraid of being laughed at.

一个人遇到不幸并非全是坏事，至少可以认清楚
谁是真正的朋友。

It´s not only an evil deed for one if he suffers misfortune, at least
he can recognize who is the true friend.

FOOD FOR THOUGHT
智慧快餐

不速之客通常只有在告辞时刻才会最受欢迎。

A dropper-in is welcome most usually while saying good-bye.

经济是一个"最坏的"老师，等于是没有上课就要
你考试了。

Economy is the 'worst' teacher. Without taking any classes, you
have to take an exam.

所谓咨询员，就是那种把你的表拿走后，再告诉你
几点钟的人。

The so-called consultant is the guy who takes away your watch
and then tells you what time it is.

聪明人说话以其经验为据，比他们更聪明的人则根据其经验而选择不说话。

Clever persons say something on the basis of their experience, the cleverer choose to say nothing according to their experience.

科学每解决一个问题后，又将因此产生十个新问题。

Every time after science has solved one problem, it brings about ten new problems.

一切运动着的事物本身都带着它自己消亡的
胚胎。

Everything in movement itself carries its own embryo of vanishing.

FOOD FOR THOUGHT

智慧快餐

何谓经验？就是每个人为自己付出的代价所取的
名字。

What is experience? It's the name everybody chooses for the
cost he pays.

FOOD FOR THOUGHT
智慧快餐

爱情是一种两个人玩的游戏,不是全赢便是皆输。

Love is a game played by two, either both win or both lose.

在人生旅途中, 要学会欣赏自己的速度和距离, 不
要被旁人所干扰。

In your life journey, you should learn to appreciate your own speed
and distance, instead of being interfered by others.

冒犯你的老板需要有勇气，冒犯你的部下只要有
气就可以了。

It needs courage to offend your boss, but just rage to your sub-
ordinate.

FOOD FOR THOUGHT
智慧快餐

不妨开发一种"人味"香水,因为有些人太缺少这
种气味了。

We might as well trial-produce a kind of "human smell" perfume,
because some people are too much short of this smell.

这个世界上的较量，其实是人的头脑在较量。

The competition of this world are actually the competition of people´s minds.

FOOD FOR THOUGHT

智慧快餐

你若能把"绊脚石"变成"垫脚石",你就是生活中的强者。

He who has the insight to turn a scar into a star is a master of his life.

水滴石穿,不是力量大,而是功夫深

Continuity of dripping water penetrates a stone not with its force
but persistency.

在竞争世界里：只有使自己成为"狼"，才能与狼
共舞。

To compete with wolves, be a wolf.

大疑大悟，小疑小悟，不疑不悟。

Big doubt leads to full awakening; small doubt leads to lesser en-
lightenment; no doubt leads to nothing.

建筑设计的灵魂——采光艺术。

The soul of architecture-lighting.

鸡不觉得人在变，人不觉得山在变。

A chicken's vision is too limited to sense a man's variation, just
as a man is to a mountain.

理财专家告诉你:你不理财,财不理你。

Advice from financiers: if you do not care for money, money does not care for you.

传闻犹如鸡蛋，经孵化会长出翅膀。

Rumor is like a hatched egg, in due course will grow wings.

FOOD FOR THOUGHT

智慧快餐

人有两只脚，钱生八只脚。

A man is only on foot, but money is footloose.

FOOD FOR THOUGHT

智慧快餐

面对争议总比面对平庸来得好。

Better controversy than mediocrity.

小心! 别用一个大错误去纠正一个小错误。

Beware not to amend a tiny error with a big mistake.

FOOD FOR THOUGHT

智慧快餐

人人都晓得要改变环境，就是不一定晓得要改变心境。

Most people know plenty about changing the environment, but few of them know about adjusting their interior.

股民与猎手同感：一鸟在手胜于二鸟在林。

Stockholders have a hunter′s instinct: one bird in hand is better
than two in the bush.

FOOD FOR THOUGHT

智慧快餐

精明的经商之术：能把尚未到手的东西，去卖给不
需要它的人。

A shrewd merchant sells item he does not own to people who
does not need it.

FOOD FOR THOUGHT

智慧快餐

人先养地，地才养人。

People nourish earth first, and then earth nourishes back.

FOOD FOR THOUGHT

智慧快餐

世上没有比脚更长的路，也没有比心更高的山。

No road is longer than your feet's reach; No mountain is higher than your heart's mount.

再版说明

　　《智慧快餐》1995 年 12 月第一版至 2001 年 2 月第 7 次印刷开本均为 36 开，第 8 次印刷开本改为 32 开，由于开本调整，增补作品 16 幅，并作为《智慧快餐》第 1 册，其余未作改动，特作说明。

——编　者

图书在版编目（ＣＩＰ）数据

智慧快餐.1:郑辛遥幽默画/郑辛遥绘.—2版.
—上海：上海人民出版社,2002
ISBN 7－208－02160－0

Ⅰ.智… Ⅱ.郑… Ⅲ.漫画-作品集-中国-现代
Ⅳ.J228.2

中国版本图书馆 CIP 数据核字(2002)第 019924 号

责任编辑　陈惠玉　　顾兆敏
翻　　译　张　磊　　姚献民　　王楚凤
封面装帧　郑辛遥

智慧快餐.1
――郑辛遥幽默画
郑辛遥 绘
世 纪 出 版 集 团
上海人民出版社出版、发行
(200001　上海福建中路193号　www.ewen.cc)
新华书店上海发行所经销
商务印书馆上海印刷股份有限公司印刷
开本 850×1168　1/32　印张 5
1995 年 11 月第 1 版　2002 年 5 月第 2 版
2002 年 5 月第 8 次印刷　印数 45,101－50,200
ISBN 7－208－02160－0/J·18
定价 15.00 元